little & LARGE
sticker activity book

MONSTER MACHINES

Miles Kelly

PUBLISHING

First published in 2006 by Miles Kelly Publishing Ltd
Bardfield Centre, Great Bardfield, Essex, CM7 4SL

Copyright © Miles Kelly Publishing Ltd 2006

This edition printed in 2008

2 4 6 8 10 9 7 5 3

Editorial Director: Belinda Gallagher

Art Director: Jo Brewer

Assistant Editor: Amanda Askew

Reprographics: Anthony Cambray, Mike Coupe, Stephan Davis, Ian Paulyn

Production Manager: Elizabeth Brunwin

British Library Cataloguing-in-Publication Data
A catalogue record for this book is available from the British Library

ISBN 978-1-84236-671-4

Printed in China

All photographs and artworks are from MKP archives

www.mileskelly.net
info@mileskelly.net

www.factsforprojects.com

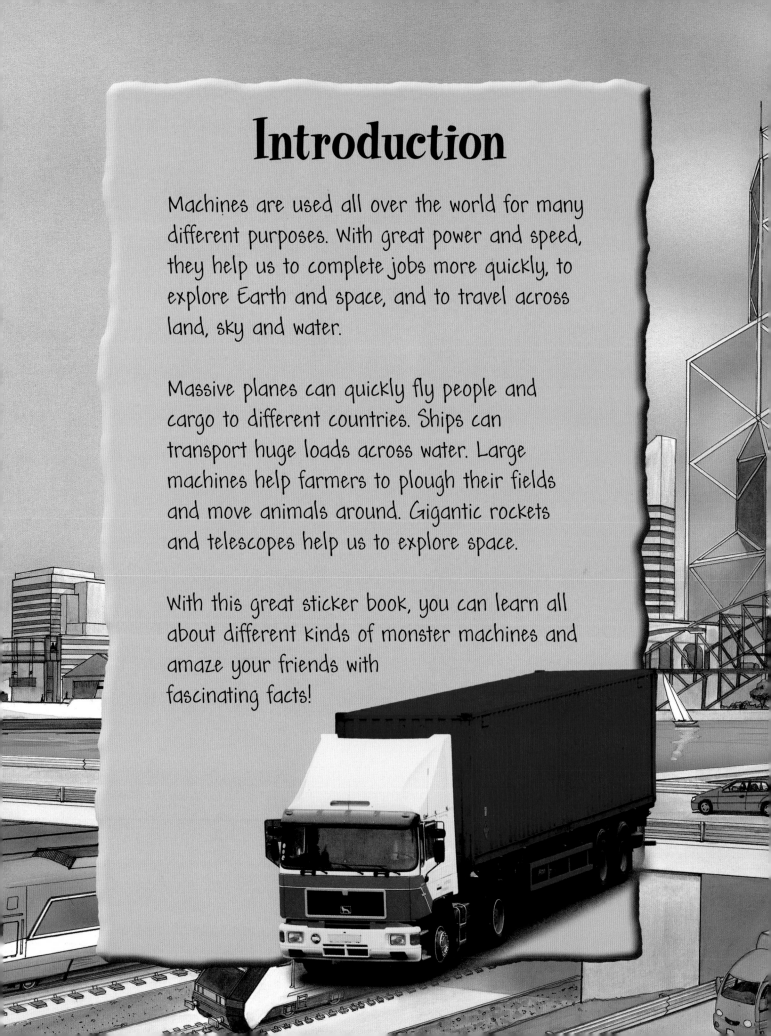

Introduction

Machines are used all over the world for many different purposes. With great power and speed, they help us to complete jobs more quickly, to explore Earth and space, and to travel across land, sky and water.

Massive planes can quickly fly people and cargo to different countries. Ships can transport huge loads across water. Large machines help farmers to plough their fields and move animals around. Gigantic rockets and telescopes help us to explore space.

With this great sticker book, you can learn all about different kinds of monster machines and amaze your friends with fascinating facts!

Mini stickers!

 Which machines do farmers use? How do we explore space? Use your mini stickers to learn all about monster machines!

Working machines – machines are used to help people in their work

On the road – many vehicles use roads or tracks, including racetracks

In space – rockets and shuttles are launched into space to investigate the Universe

On the water – ships move heavy loads and people – they are also war machines

In the air – gigantic planes zoom through the air, often taking people on holiday

Working machines

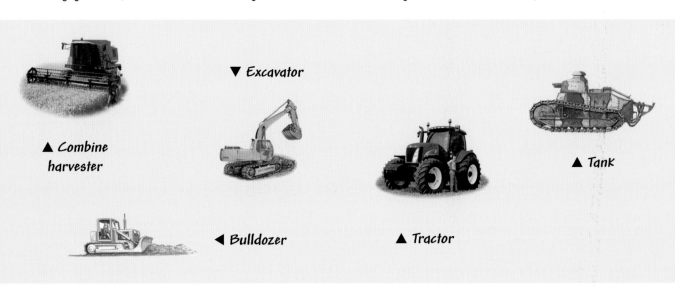

▲ Combine harvester

▼ Excavator

◄ Bulldozer

▲ Tractor

▲ Tank

On the road

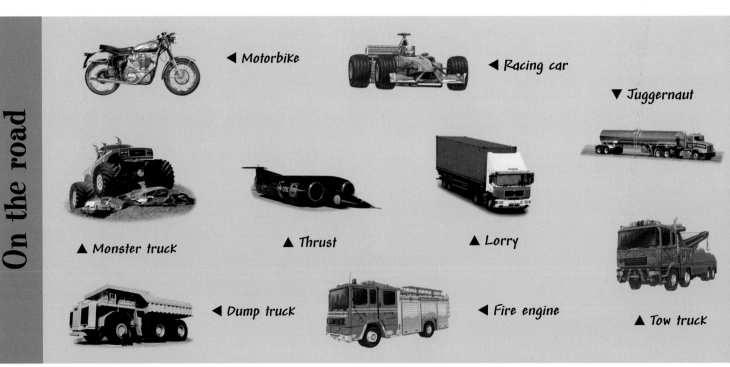

◄ Motorbike

◄ Racing car

▼ Juggernaut

▲ Monster truck

▲ Thrust

▲ Lorry

◄ Dump truck

◄ Fire engine

▲ Tow truck

In space

▲ Space shuttle

▶ Saturn V

▼ Apollo II

▲ Hubble space telescope

On the water

▲ Submarine

▲ Queen Elizabeth II

▶ Oil tanker

▲ Frigate

▲ Bismarck

◀ Hovercraft

◀ Freedom ship

▲ Destroyer

In the air

▲ Helicopter

▲ Hindenburg

▼ Observation balloon

▲ Concorde

▶ Stealth

▲ Jumbo jet

Monster machines

 ▼ Excavator

This mighty machine has a large shovel to dig up and move tonnes of earth

▲ Fire engine

This emergency vehicle carries vast quantities of water, hoses and a crane – the fire service can put out fires and rescue people in high buildings

▲ Space shuttle

A space shuttle takes astronauts from Earth to space stations out in space

 ▼ Observation balloon

During World War I, this huge balloon allowed watchmen to see where the enemy army was situated and what they were doing

▲ Hovercraft

First developed in 1959, the hovercraft moves across land or water on a cushion of air

▲ Combine harvester

Farmers use this machine to cut grain and separate the grain's seeds from the straw

 ▲ Submarine

Belonging to the German navy, this submarine was armed with torpedoes, and used in wartime

▶ Dump truck

Carrying heavy loads, the back of this truck lifts up to dump its contents

KEY:

 Working machines

 On the road

 In space

 On the water

 In the air

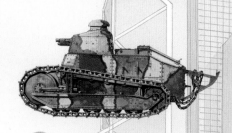

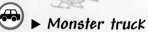

▶ Monster truck

A gigantic truck with very large tyres, it is often used for races and exhibitions

▲ Tank

Used in war, a tank has heavy armour and guns – the first tank was developed in 1916 for World War I

◀ Juggernaut

This huge truck is used to transport great quantities of liquid, such as oil

▶ Freedom ship

A floating city, this ship has its own hotel, shops, casino and even a school

▲ Tow truck

With its special equipment, this vehicle tows away cars that have broken down

◀ Destroyer

A powerful warship with guns, missiles and torpedoes – it escorted and defended a group of ships against attack

◀ Saturn V rocket

This rocket carried the spacecraft of the first men to land on the Moon – it weighed over 2700 tonnes

◀ Jumbo jet

Carrying up to 600 passengers, the jumbo jet flies at about 900 kilometres an hour

The longest car in the world is so long, it has a swimming pool inside it!

Space study

The International Space Station is the largest space station ever built. Sixteen countries are helping to build it, including the US, Russia, Japan, Canada, Brazil and 11 European countries. The first section, Zarya, was launched on 20 November 1998 – sections are continuously being added.

The crew live onboard for several months at a time. The first crew of three people arrived at the space station in November 2000 and stayed for over four months. When the station is finished, there will be room for seven astronauts and it will measure over 100 metres across and 90 metres long, with giant solar panels to provide electricity.

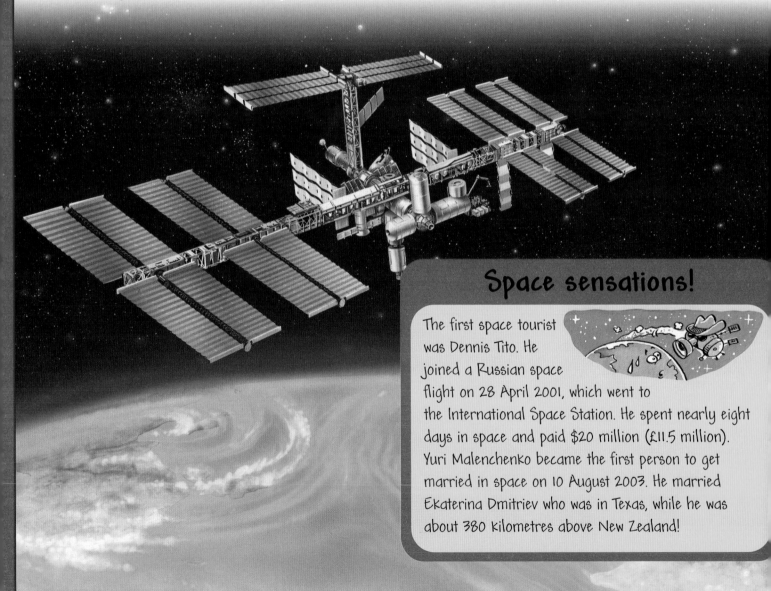

Space sensations!

The first space tourist was Dennis Tito. He joined a Russian space flight on 28 April 2001, which went to the International Space Station. He spent nearly eight days in space and paid $20 million (£11.5 million). Yuri Malenchenko became the first person to get married in space on 10 August 2003. He married Ekaterina Dmitriev who was in Texas, while he was about 380 kilometres above New Zealand!

Monster machines

▲ Combine harvester

▲ Excavator

▲ Dump truck

▲ Fire engine

▲ Space shuttle

▲ Observation balloon

▲ Submarine

▲ Hovercraft

▼ Combine harvester

► Excavator

▼ Fire engine

▲ Dump truck

► Space shuttle

◄ Observation balloon

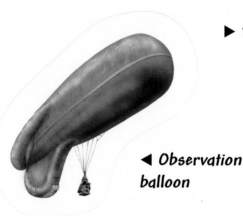

▼ Submarine

▲ Hovercraft

Monster machines

▲ Tank

▲ Monster truck

▲ Juggernaut

▲ Tow truck

▲ Freedom ship

▲ Destroyer

▲ Saturn V

▲ Jumbo jet

▼ Tank

▲ Monster truck

▶ Juggernaut

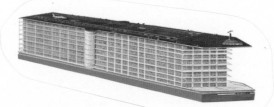
▲ Freedom ship

▲ Tow truck

◀ Destroyer

▲ Saturn V

▶ Jumbo jet

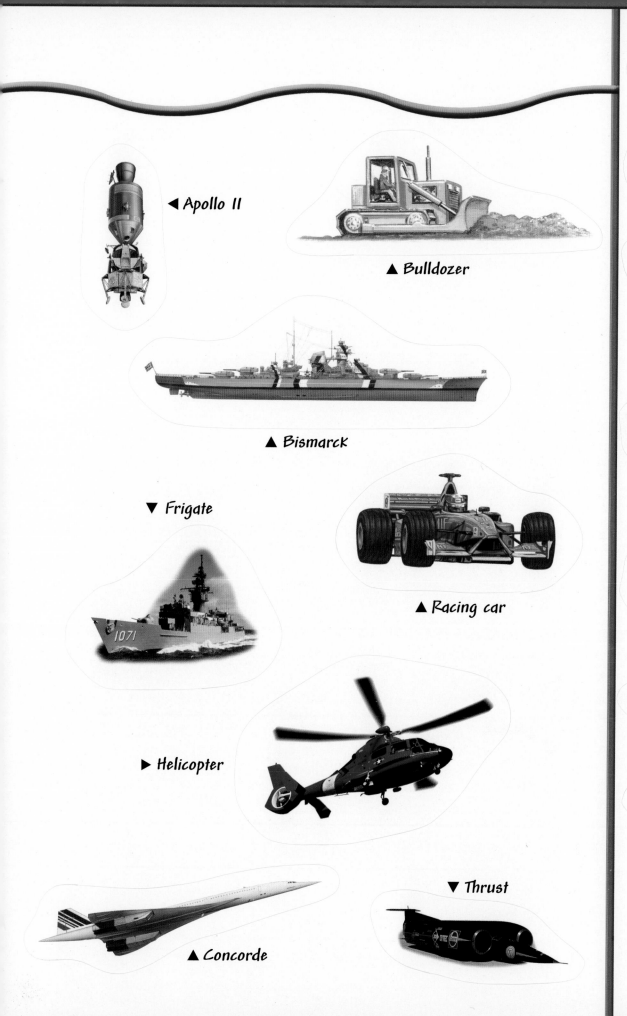

◀ Apollo II

▲ Bulldozer

▲ Bismarck

▼ Frigate

▲ Racing car

▶ Helicopter

▼ Thrust

▲ Concorde

▲ Bulldozer

▲ Racing car

▲ Thrust

▲ Frigate

▲ Helicopter

▲ Bismarck

▲ Concorde

▲ Apollo II

Monster machines

▲ Tractor

▼ Motorbike

▶ Lorry

▼ Hubble space telescope

▲ Stealth

▼ Queen Elizabeth II

▼ Hindenburg

▲ Oil tanker

▲ Tractor

▲ Motorbike

▲ Lorry

▲ Hubble space
telescope

▲ Stealth

▲ Queen Elizabeth II

▲ Hindenburg

▲ Oil tanker

Water runway

Aircraft carriers are huge warships. At over 300 metres long, they carry up to 85 military planes and need a large crew. Their flat top deck is a runway for take-offs and landings of fighter and bomber planes. The runway is actually quite small, so steam-powered catapults are used to launch the planes into the air. These catapults help planes to accelerate from 0 to 240 kilometres an hour in just two seconds.

The United States owns 12 carriers – the most in the world. Few countries have them as they are very expensive. The most famous is the US *Abraham Lincoln*. Most countries today use light carriers. These are less expensive because they are smaller and do not need catapults. They support aircraft such as helicopters and jump jets.

▼ As well as enabling military planes to take-off and land at sea, aircraft carriers also protect other warships from attack by air or sea.

Monster machines

 **▲ Bulldozer**

A powerful tractor, the bulldozer has a large blade to flatten ground and buildings

 **▲ Apollo 11**

This Apollo mission was the first manned mission to land on the Moon in 1969

▼ Thrust

In 1997, *Thrust* was the first vehicle to break the sound barrier on land – it reached 1228 kilometres an hour

▼ Racing car

This single-seater car is used for Formula 1 racing and can reach speeds of about 300 kilometres an hour

◄ Helicopter

The rotating blades enable the helicopter to fly – it can only reach 400 kilometres an hour

► Frigate

This warship is mainly used to escort other ships – it provides protection against attack

▼ Bismarck

A World War II German battleship, *Bismarck* weighed 43,000 tonnes and carried eight 350-mm (15-inch) guns – she sank in battle on 27 May 1941

▲ Concorde

This supersonic plane began transatlantic flights in 1976 and retired in 2003 – it could reach over 2170 kilometres an hour

KEY:

Working machines

On the road

In space

On the water

In the air

 ▼ **Tractor**

Used by farmers, this vehicle has large tyres – it is used for pulling farm machinery

▲ **Motorbike**

First developed in 1885 in Germany, the motorbike is used for racing as well as everyday travel

▼ **Lorry**

This large truck is used to transport heavy goods, often for shops and businesses

▼ **Stealth**

Used largely in the Gulf War (1991), the stealth is designed to not be seen by radars, which makes it difficult to detect during a war attack

◄ **Queen Elizabeth II**

With her first voyage in 1969, the 'QE2' can carry nearly 3000 people – she even has her own library and hospital

▼ **Oil tanker**

This ship is designed to carry a large amount of oil across the ocean

► **Hindenburg**

In 1937, Hindenburg, a huge airship filled with hydrogen gas, exploded and was destroyed in less than one minute – 36 people died

▲ **Hubble space telescope**

Orbiting the Earth since 1990, the Hubble sends clear images to scientists, which have enabled them to make many new discoveries

The world's longest truck, the Arctic Snow Train, is over 170 metres in length and has 54 wheels. It needs a team of six drivers!

The biggest and best!

Read on to find out about some fast record-breaking facts

The Ford GT-90 has a top speed of 378 kilometres an hour and zooms from 0 to 100 kilometres an hour in 3.2 seconds.

The first locomotive to reach up to 160 kilometres an hour was the *City of Truro* in 1904.

On 20 March 1999, the first round-the-world hot-air balloon flight was completed by Bertan Piccard and Brian Jones.

• France's *TGV Atlantique* is the world's fastest train. Between the towns of Courtalain and Tours in 1990, it set a record speed on a national rail system of 515.3 kilometres an hour.

• On 10 April 1912, the *Titanic* began her maiden voyage. At 53,000 tonnes and 269 metres in length, she was the biggest passenger ship in the world. Four days later, she hit an iceberg. It only took 2.5 hours for the ship to sink.

• The Porsche 911 turbo was the fastest accelerating car for almost 20 years after it was launched in 1975. It could go from 0 to 100 kilometres an hour in just 5.4 seconds.

The city of New York, USA, has 466 underground railway stations – that's more than any other city in the world.

Discover interesting facts about the invention of the greatest machines

• The world's first petrol-engine car was built by Karl Benz in 1885. It had three wheels and was steered by a lever at the front. Chains from the engine drove the back wheels. Its top speed was only 16 kilometres an hour.

• *Rocket* became the first ever intercity locomotive. It was designed and built by two British engineers, George and Robert Stephenson. It could reach speeds of nearly 60 kilometres an hour.

• Orville and Wilbur Wright built the world's first plane, the *Flyer*. Its first flight lasted 12 seconds and it travelled 37 metres. In 1903, they completed the first controlled aeroplane flight in the *Kittyhawk*.

The biggest vehicles ever built are two Marion crawlers, used to move rockets. They weigh 8000 tonnes.

The largest ship ever is the *Jahre Viking*, at 564,763 tonnes in weight and 485 metres long.

Only 16 Concorde planes were ever built. They could cross the Atlantic in under three hours.

A bobsleigh can travel at over 130 kilometres an hour along a track made of solid ice.

Fun facts

🚀 The Airbus A380 will be the world's biggest airliner when it is launched in 2006. It will carry about 555 passengers on three decks.

🚀 Maglev trains of the future, suspended by powerful magnets, will reach speeds of 800 kilometres an hour.

🚀 The Hawker Harrier of 1968 is the only jet that can take-off vertically.

Test your memory!

How much can you remember from your monster machines sticker activity book? Find out below!

1. How many passengers can a jumbo jet carry?
2. When was the International Space Station launched?
3. Which vehicle broke the sound barrier in 1997?
4. What is a monster truck used for?
5. Can a hovercraft only be used on land?
6. In which year was the *Titanic's* maiden voyage?
7. Who was the first space tourist?
8. What is the most famous aircraft carrier?
9. How long is the world's longest truck?
10. How does a helicopter fly?
11. Who built the world's first plane?
12. What equipment does a fire engine carry?

The first hydrogen balloon was attacked and destroyed by terrified farm workers when it landed in 1783. It had only flown 24 kilometres.

13. When was the first tank developed?
14. How is the International Space Station powered?
15. What launches planes from aircraft carriers?
16. In which country was the motorbike first developed?
17. What is the world's fastest train?
18. In which year did the *Hindenburg* explode?
19. How fast could Concorde travel?
20. What was the first manned mission to land on the Moon?

The first submarine was developed in 1620. It was a rowing boat covered with waterproof skins.

In 1980, a US Navy hovercraft reached a record speed of 170 kilometres an hour – faster than any warship has ever travelled.

The Red Arrows need perfect timing to perform stunts and close formation at air shows.

Answers:

1. Up to 600 2. 20 November 1998 3. Thrust
4. Races and exhibitions 5. No, on water, too 6. 1912
7. Dennis Tito 8. US Abraham Lincoln
9. Over 110 metres 10. Using rotating blades
11. Orville and Wilbur Wright 12. Hoses, a crane and vast quantities of water 13. In 1916 for World War I
14. Through solar panels that create electricity
15. Catapults 16. Germany 17. France's TGV Atlantique
18. 1937 19. 2110 kilometres an hour 20. Apollo 11

The largest tankers are over half a kilometre long. Sailors travel from one end of the tanker to another by bicycle.

Other sticker books

You can now have even more fun and collect
all the sticker books in this series

978-1-84236-660-8

978-1-84236-661-5

978-1-84236-303-4

978-1-84236-244-0

978-1-84236-513-7

978-1-84236-304-1

978-1-84236-305-8

978-1-84236-662-2

978-1-84236-302-7

978-1-84236-663-9

978-1-84236-514-4

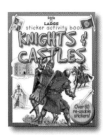

978-1-84236-255-6

978-1-84236-671-4

978-1-84236-246-4

978-1-84236-307-2

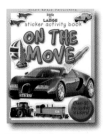

978-1-84236-245-7

978-1-84236-306-5

978-1-84236-669-1

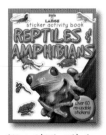

978-1-84236-254-9

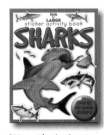

978-1-84236-512-0

978-1-84236-247-1

978-1-84236-515-1

978-1-84236-668-4

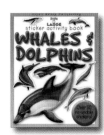

978-1-84236-672-1

978-1-84236-498-7